The Wild Cat Guide

Written by Claire Llewellyn

Contents

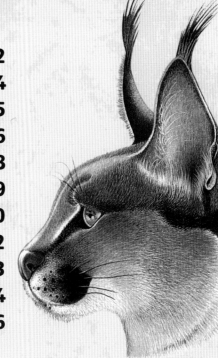

Looking at cats

The cat family

There are 35 **species** of cat. Five of these are **big cats** –
cheetah, jaguar, leopard, lion and tiger. The others are
small cats, including the cats people keep as pets.
Most cats are **wild**. All cats are **mammals**.

A cat's body

Wild cats are hunters.
They have to catch every
meal. A cat's body is slim
and strong and helps the
animal to hunt. It can
think fast, run fast and
kill fast!

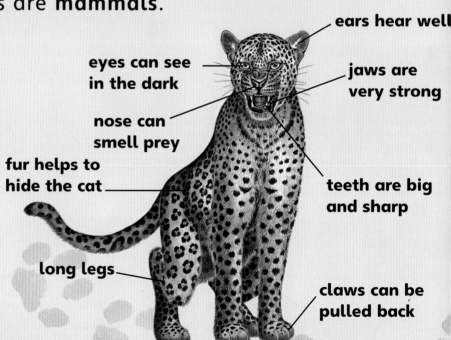

ears hear well

eyes can see
in the dark

jaws are
very strong

nose can
smell prey

fur helps to
hide the cat

teeth are big
and sharp

long legs

claws can be
pulled back

A cat's fur

A wild cat's fur helps it to hunt. It helps the cat to hide from its **prey**. Spots and stripes are hard to see in forests or long grass.

Jaguar

Tiger

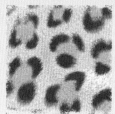
Leopard

The tiger's stripes make it hard to see in the forest.

3

Bobcat

The bobcat lives in the hills of North America. It hides in a **den** by day, and comes out to hunt at night. It feeds on rabbits, birds and other small animals.

white spots on ears

thick coat of fur

short tail

large paws

Caracal

The caracal lives in the dry parts of Africa and Asia.
It has black ears with long **tufts** of hair at the tips.
It is very good at catching birds. As the bird takes off,
the caracal jumps up into the air and hits it
with its paws.

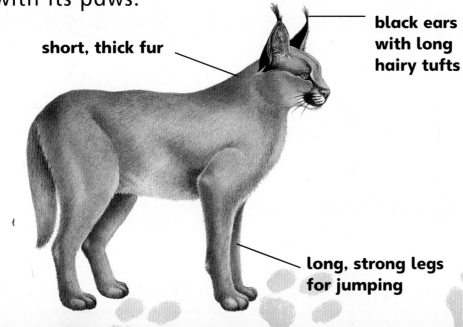

short, thick fur

black ears
with long
hairy tufts

long, strong legs
for jumping

Cheetah

The cheetah lives on the open **grasslands** of Africa. It hunts animals such as **antelope**. Antelope run fast, but the cheetah is the fastest animal in the world. It can run at up to 95 kilometres an hour, but only for a very short time. If it doesn't catch its prey quickly, it must give up and try again later.

short ears

small head

black line from mouth to eye

slim body

long, slim legs

Did you know?
Cheetahs are the only cats that can't pull in their claws.

A cheetah about to catch its prey

Jaguar

The jaguar lives in the thick forests of South America. Unlike many cats, it likes water and can swim. It eats fish and water animals, as well as deer and other forest animals.

A jaguar resting in the forest undergrowth

rings of spots   strong body

short, strong legs

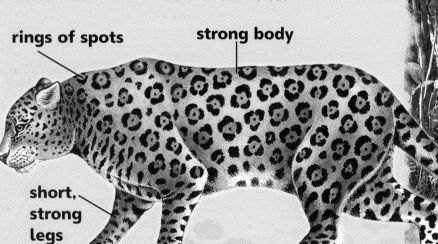

Leopard

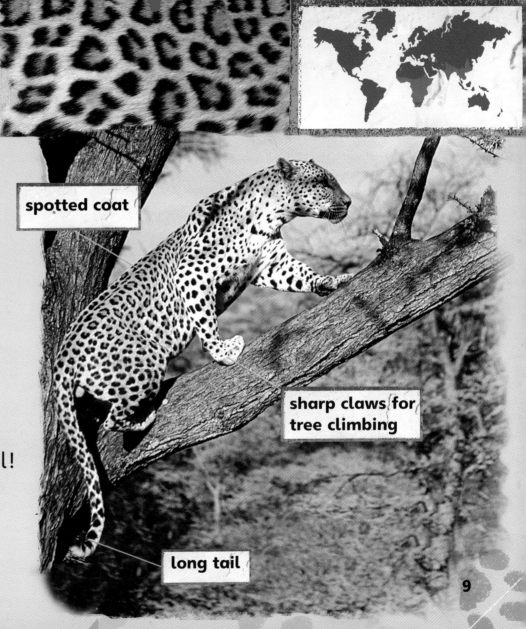

The leopard is the smallest big cat. It lives in Africa and Asia. It is very good at climbing trees. When it kills an animal, it drags its body up a tree. This stops other animals from stealing its meal!

spotted coat

sharp claws for tree climbing

long tail

Lion

The lion lives on the dry grasslands of Africa. Most cats live alone, but lions live in families called prides. There are between 10 and 30 lions in a pride. The females, known as lionesses, do most of the hunting. Lionesses don't have a mane, but male lions do.

A pride of lions

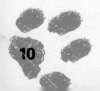

male

female

A lioness waiting to pounce

male lions have a mane

Puma

The puma lives in North and South America.
It is the biggest of the small cats. When it kills
an animal, it eats some of the meat, then it hides
the rest away to eat later.

brown fur

A puma with its next meal

long tail
with
black tip

long back legs

white fur
under nose

Snow leopard

The snow leopard lives in the cold, snowy mountains of Asia. It has a thick fur coat to keep it warm, and large, furry paws to stop it sinking in the snow. It feeds on wild goats, deer and other mountain animals.

warm coat

pale fur helps it to hide in the snow

long, furry tail

big, furry paws

Tiger

Tigers are the biggest cats in the world. They live in forests in parts of Asia. Baby tigers are called **cubs**. New cubs feed on their mother's milk, but after six months they feed on meat. As they get bigger, the cubs like to play. They creep up and jump on one another. This is how they learn to hunt.

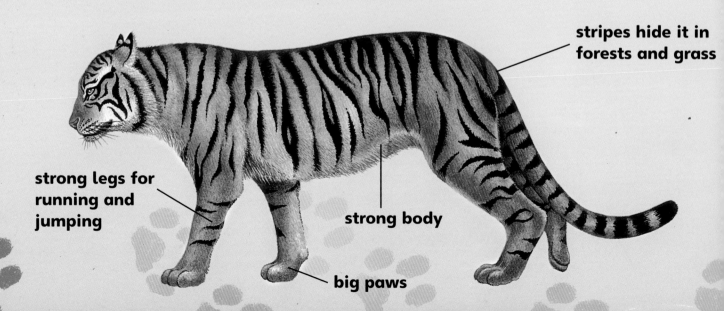

stripes hide it in forests and grass

strong legs for running and jumping

strong body

big paws

Like the jaguar, the tiger can swim.

Did you know?
A tiger's biggest teeth are 9 cm long – about as long as a child's hand.

Wild cats carry cubs in their mouth.

Glossary

antelope	a family of grass-eating mammals, such as gazelles
big cats	the five biggest types of cat – lion, tiger, cheetah, jaguar and leopard
cubs	the babies of wild cats
den	a wild animal's home, often a cave
grasslands	land covered by grass, such as in Africa
mammals	animals that grow fur and feed milk to their babies
prey	an animal which is killed by another animal for food
small cats	types of cats other than big cats
species	a type of animal or plant
tufts	small bunches of hair
wild	not tamed or kept by people